# Maths BASICS

OR AGES
6-7
KEY STAGE 1

## Contents

| | |
|---|---|
| Read and write numbers to 100 | 3 |
| Addition | 4 |
| Money: totalling | 5 |
| 2D shapes | 6 |
| Counting sequences within 50 | 7 |
| Subtraction: finding differences | 8 |
| Multiplication: repeated addition | 9 |
| Sharing | 10 |
| Time | 11 |
| Data: block graphs | 12 |
| Breaking up numbers | 13 |
| Subtraction facts | 14 |
| Money: giving change | 15 |
| 3D shapes | 16 |
| Counting patterns | 17 |
| Decade sums | 18 |
| 2 times table | 19 |
| Fractions: halves and quarters | 20 |
| Measures: length | 21 |
| Data: pictograms | 22 |
| Comparing and ordering numbers | 23 |
| Addition and subtraction | 24 |
| Problems | 25 |
| Shapes | 26 |
| Odd and even numbers | 27 |
| Money and place value | 28 |
| 10 times table | 29 |
| Fractions of quantities | 30 |
| Time | 31 |
| Data: tables | 32 |
| Answers | |

# How to use this book

**Numeracy Basics** helps you to help your child practise many important basic skills covered in the *National Numeracy Strategy* and *National Curriculum*.

Each book is divided into *30 units* of work which focus on *one clear* objective.

Most of the units are designed using the same easy-to-follow *key features*. In some cases these features are combined into one activity, offering further practice where appropriate.

**Title**
Target learning objective.

**Look and learn**
Introduces and explains the target objective. Provides an example to illustrate it.

**Practice**
Provides straightforward practice activities based on the target objective.

**Challenge**
Provides activities to extend and challenge.

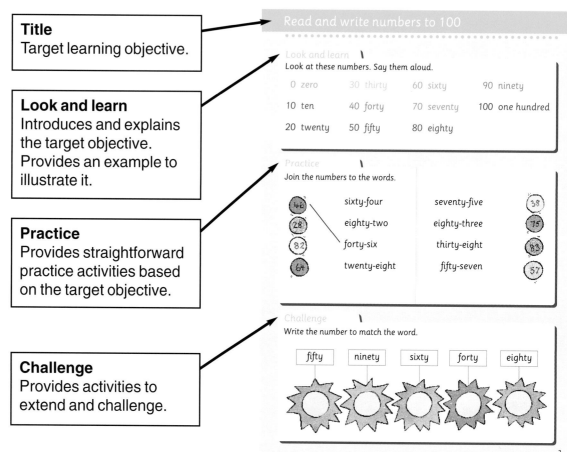

## Suggested way of using the book

- It is suggested that your child works systematically through the book.
- Try tackling one unit per week.
- Read through and discuss the *Look and learn* section with your child to make sure the key objective is understood.

- Help your child get started on the Practice section.
- After this, your child can start to work fairly independently through the page, but will need further support and encouragement.
- The answers are supplied at the end of the book for checking each unit on its completion.

# Enjoy the book!

## Look and learn

Look at these numbers. Say them aloud.

| | | | |
|---|---|---|---|
| 0 zero | 30 thirty | 60 sixty | 90 ninety |
| 10 ten | 40 forty | 70 seventy | 100 one hundred |
| 20 twenty | 50 fifty | 80 eighty | |

## Practice

Join the numbers to the words.

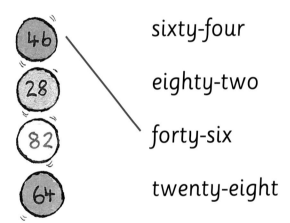

sixty-four

eighty-two

forty-six

twenty-eight

seventy-five

eighty-three

thirty-eight

fifty-seven

## Challenge

Write the number to match the word.

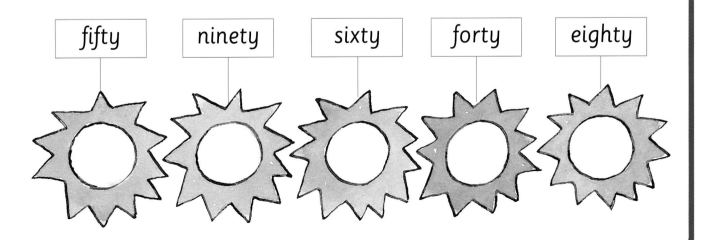

| fifty | ninety | sixty | forty | eighty |

3

## Look and learn

A number line helps with addition. It helps to count along it.

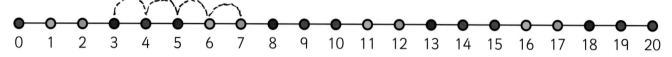

0  1  2  3  4  5  6  7  8  9  10  11  12  13  14  15  16  17  18  19  20

For example, 3 + 4 = 7

## Practice

Fill in the missing numbers.

4 + ⬤ = 11     ⬤ + 4 = 14     ⬤ + 2 = 17

8 + ⬤ = 18     ⬤ + 8 = 11     12 + ⬤ = 15

5 + ⬤ = 13     ⬤ + 9 = 17     13 + ⬤ = 16

7 + ⬤ = 14     ⬤ + 3 = 12     ⬤ + 4 = 19

## Challenge

Complete the tables showing the numbers going into and coming out of the number machines.

| in | 2 | | | 8 |
|---|---|---|---|---|
| out | | 8 | 10 | |

| in | 3 | 8 | | |
|---|---|---|---|---|
| out | | | 10 | 12 |

## Look and learn

A money number track will help with totalling coins.

## Practice

Complete the prices.

| | | | | | |
|---|---|---|---|---|---|
| ball | _____ | yo-yo | _____ | sweet | _____ |
| pencil | _____ | whistle | _____ | pen | _____ |
| rubber | _____ | hat | _____ | ruler | _____ |
| **total** | _____ | **total** | _____ | **total** | _____ |

## Challenge

Draw coins to make each set equal £1.

# 2D shapes

## Look and learn

Look at these shapes. Are any familiar? It is useful to remember what they are called.

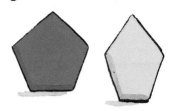

**pentagons**
**5-sided shapes**

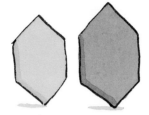

**hexagons**
**6-sided shapes**

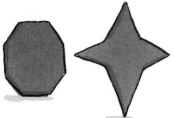

**octagons**
**8-sided shapes**

## Practice

Join the names to the shape.

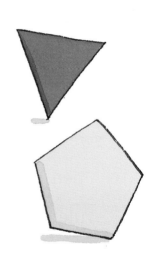

triangle

square

pentagon

hexagon

octagon

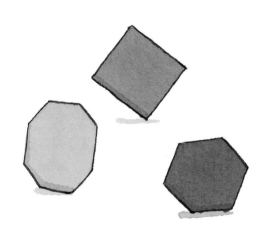

## Challenge

Tick the odd one out in each set.

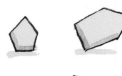

All pentagons have

◻ sides.

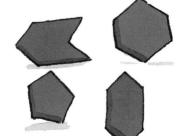

All hexagons have

◻ sides.

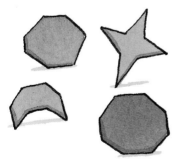

All octagons have

◻ sides.

6

## Look and learn

Use the grid to help with counting sequences.

| 1 | 2 | 3 | 4 | 5 | 6 | 7 | 8 | 9 | 10 |
|---|---|---|---|---|---|---|---|---|----|
| 11 | 12 | 13 | 14 | 15 | 16 | 17 | 18 | 19 | 20 |
| 21 | 22 | 23 | 24 | 25 | 26 | 27 | 28 | 29 | 30 |
| 31 | 32 | 33 | 34 | 35 | 36 | 37 | 38 | 39 | 40 |
| 41 | 42 | 43 | 44 | 45 | 46 | 47 | 48 | 49 | 50 |

## Practice

Write the missing numbers on the scarves.

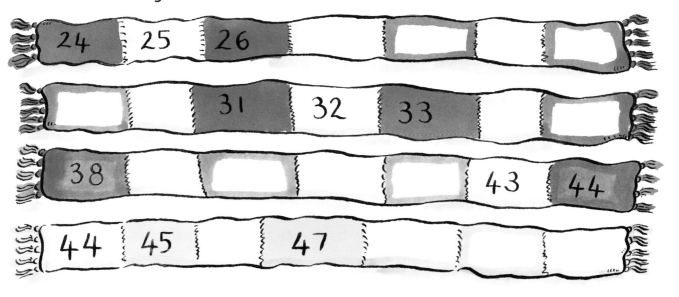

## Challenge

Write the missing numbers in the circles.

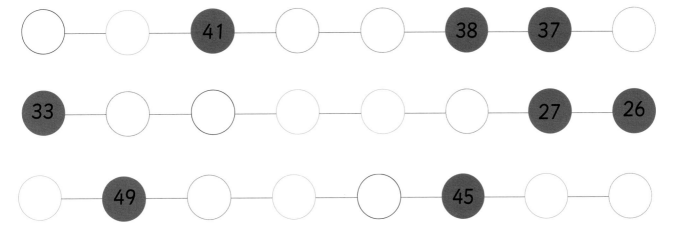

## Look and learn

Counting in jumps can help to work sums out.

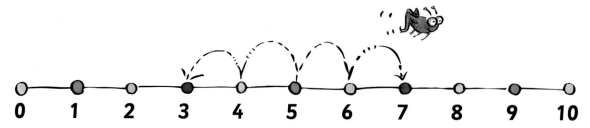

The difference between 3 and 7 is 4.

## Practice

Draw the jumps to find the differences.

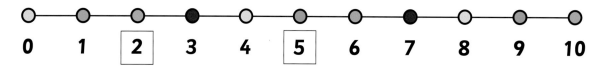

The difference between 2 and 5 is ☐

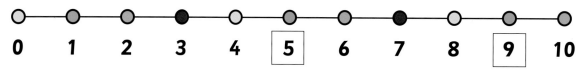

The difference between 5 and 9 is ☐

## Challenge

Write the differences between these numbers.

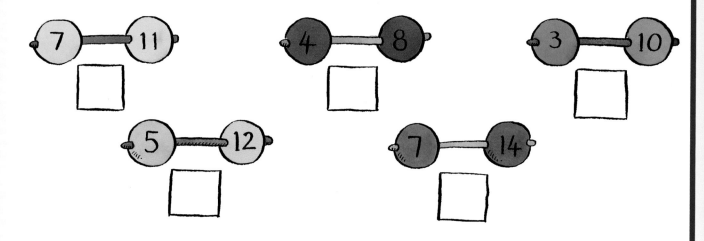

## Look and learn

 +  +  +

3 + 3 + 3 + 3

4 lots of 3 are **12**

## Practice

Write how many:

[ ] toes on two feet

[ ] legs on 2 horses

[ ] eyes on 4 owls

[ ] feet on 3 ducks

[ ] cakes on 3 plates

[ ] eggs in 4 nests

## Challenge

Show the jumps on the number lines.

3 jumps of 2 is [ ]

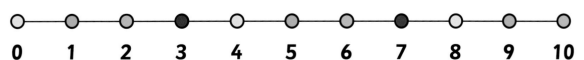

0   1   2   3   4   5   6   7   8   9   10

4 jumps of 2 is [ ]

0   1   2   3   4   5   6   7   8   9   10

### Look and learn

It is important to know how to share things equally.

12 sweets among 3 children.      5 sweets among 2 children.

### Practice

Share these equally.

 shells in 2 buckets      ☐ shells in 3 buckets

 flags on 2 sandcastles      ☐ flags on 3 sandcastles

### Challenge

Divide the apples between 2 plates. Draw them on.

☐ apples on each plate

# Time

## Look and learn

These pairs of clocks show the same times.

## Practice

Write the times.

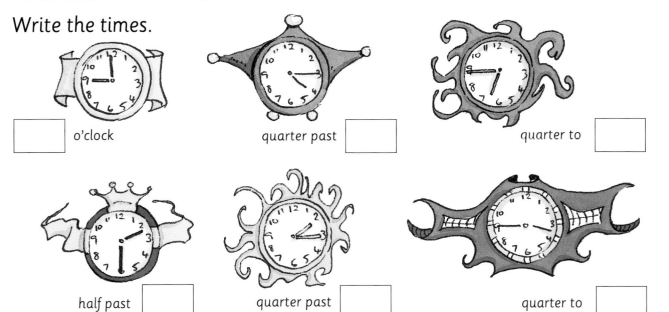

o'clock

quarter past

quarter to

half past

quarter past

quarter to

## Challenge

Join the clocks that say the same time.

## Look and learn

This graph shows the favourite colours of 12 children.

The children's favourite colour was red.

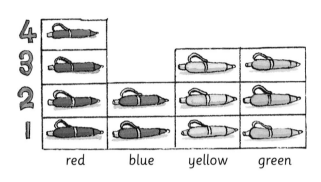

red    blue    yellow    green

## Practice

This graph shows the colour of house doors.

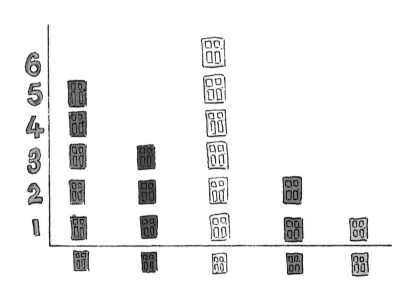

How many doors are red? ☐

How many doors are white? ☐

There are ☐ more brown doors than blue doors.

How many doors are there altogether? ☐

Collect data to draw your own graph, showing favourite pets.

## Look and learn

It is fun to spot patterns in numbers.
Look at these. What pattern can you see?

$25 = 20 + 5$   $28 = 20 + 8$   $31 = 30 + 1$

$26 = 20 + 6$   $29 = 20 + 9$   $32 = 30 + 2$

$27 = 20 + 7$   $30 = 30 + 0$   $33 = 30 + 3$

## Practice

Write the missing numbers in the boxes.

$27 = 20 + \boxed{\phantom{0}}$   $62 = 60 + \boxed{\phantom{0}}$   $42 = \boxed{\phantom{0}} + 2$

$34 = 30 + \boxed{\phantom{0}}$   $73 = 70 + \boxed{\phantom{0}}$   $54 = 50 + \boxed{\phantom{0}}$

$38 = 30 + \boxed{\phantom{0}}$   $79 = 70 + \boxed{\phantom{0}}$   $72 = \boxed{\phantom{0}} + 2$

$47 = 40 + \boxed{\phantom{0}}$   $81 = 80 + \boxed{\phantom{0}}$   $64 = 60 + \boxed{\phantom{0}}$

$59 = 50 + \boxed{\phantom{0}}$   $99 = 90 + \boxed{\phantom{0}}$   $86 = \boxed{\phantom{0}} + 6$

## Challenge

Write the numbers shown on each abacus.

| tens    units | tens    units | tens    units | tens    units |
|---|---|---|---|
| 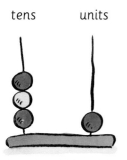 | 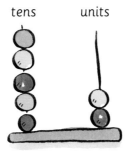 | 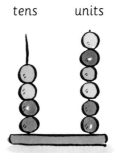 |  |
|  |  |  | |

## Look and learn

A number line can help with subtraction. It helps to count back along it.

0 1 2 3 4 5 6 7 8 9 10 11 12 13 14 15 16 17 18 19 20

*Try counting along it with your finger.*

## Practice

Write the missing numbers in the televisions.

$8 - 3 = \boxed{\phantom{0}}$

$7 - 4 = \boxed{\phantom{0}}$

$4 - 1 = \boxed{\phantom{0}}$

$9 - 2 = \boxed{\phantom{0}}$

$6 - 3 = \boxed{\phantom{0}}$

$\boxed{\phantom{0}} - 4 = 6$

$\boxed{\phantom{0}} - 3 = 4$

$\boxed{\phantom{0}} - 6 = 2$

$\boxed{\phantom{0}} - 6 = 5$

$\boxed{\phantom{0}} - 5 = 3$

$9 - \boxed{\phantom{0}} = 3$

$4 - \boxed{\phantom{0}} = 2$

$8 - \boxed{\phantom{0}} = 1$

$7 - \boxed{\phantom{0}} = 5$

$10 - \boxed{\phantom{0}} = 7$

## Challenge

Complete the tables for these number machines.

| in | 6 | | 9 | 15 |
|----|---|---|---|----|
| out | | 3 | | |

| in | | 7 | | |
|-----|---|---|---|----|
| out | 4 | | 8 | 12 |

## Look and learn

When you buy things, you will often be given some change. It is useful to be able to check it is right.

Each of these coins has a special shape. This makes them easy to spot.

## Practice

£1 is paid for each toy. Draw the coins you might be given as change.

## Challenge

Here is the change given from £1. What did each toy cost?

cost ▢ p          cost ▢ p          cost ▢ p

## Look and learn

Can you see these shapes all around you? Practise naming them.

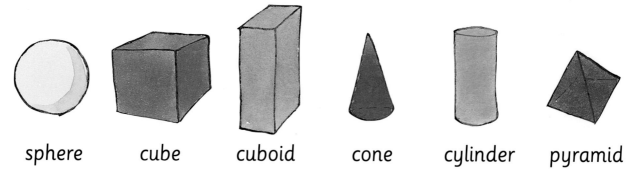

sphere    cube    cuboid    cone    cylinder    pyramid

## Practice

Join each shape to its name.

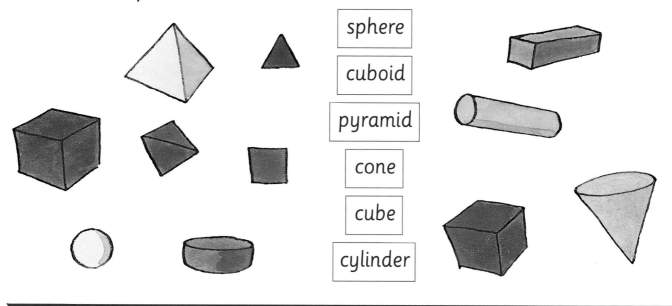

sphere

cuboid

pyramid

cone

cube

cylinder

## Challenge

Join the shapes to their faces.

# Counting patterns

## Look and learn

Look at the number grid. Can you see any patterns?

| 1 | 2 | 3 | 4 | 5 | 6 | 7 | 8 | 9 | 10 |
|---|---|---|---|---|---|---|---|---|---|
| 11 | 12 | 13 | 14 | 15 | 16 | 17 | 18 | 19 | 20 |
| 21 | 22 | 23 | 24 | 25 | 26 | 27 | 28 | 29 | 30 |
| 31 | 32 | 33 | 34 | 35 | 36 | 37 | 38 | 39 | 40 |
| 41 | 42 | 43 | 44 | 45 | 46 | 47 | 48 | 49 | 50 |

## Practice

Count in twos and write the next 3 numbers.

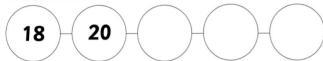
18 — 20 — ◯ — ◯ — ◯

28 — 30 — ◯ — ◯ — ◯

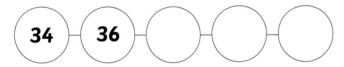
34 — 36 — ◯ — ◯ — ◯

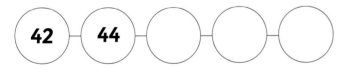
42 — 44 — ◯ — ◯ — ◯

Count in fives and write the next 3 numbers.

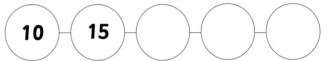
10 — 15 — ◯ — ◯ — ◯

25 — 30 — ◯ — ◯ — ◯

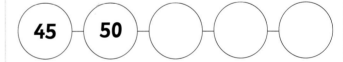
45 — 50 — ◯ — ◯ — ◯

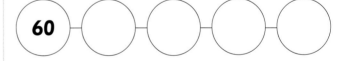
60 — ◯ — ◯ — ◯

## Challenge

Count in threes and write the next 4 numbers.

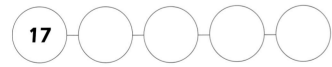
17 — ◯ — ◯ — ◯ — ◯

27 — ◯ — ◯ — ◯ — ◯

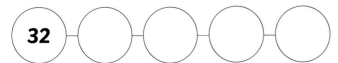
32 — ◯ — ◯ — ◯ — ◯

Count in fours and write the next 4 numbers.

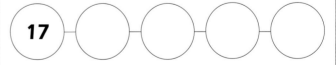
17 — ◯ — ◯ — ◯ — ◯

29 — ◯ — ◯ — ◯ — ◯

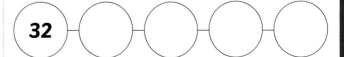
32 — ◯ — ◯ — ◯ — ◯

# Decade sums

## Look and learn

Look at this number pattern. Read it aloud.

## Practice

Write in the missing numbers.

10 + 10 → ☐ + 30 → ☐ – 20 → ☐ – 20 → 10

20 + 40 → ☐ – 30 → ☐ – 20 → ☐ + 10 → 20

30 – 10 → ☐ + 40 → ☐ – 40 → ☐ + 10 → 30

40 + 30 → ☐ – 20 → ☐ – 30 → ☐ + 30 → 50

## Challenge

The three corner numbers add up to 100. Write the missing number.

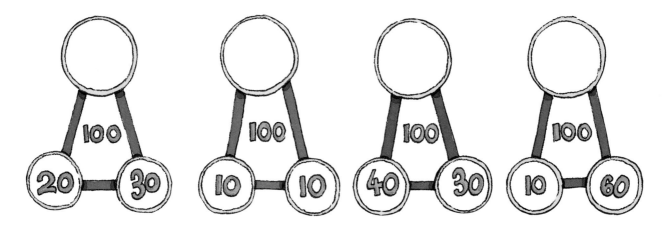

18

## Look and learn

Look at the 2 times table. Read it aloud.

| | | | | | | | | | |
|---|---|---|---|---|---|---|---|---|---|
| 1 × 2 | 2 × 1 | 2 | 5 × 2 | 2 × 5 | 10 | 9 × 2 | 2 × 9 | 18 |
| 2 × 2 | 2 × 2 | 4 | 6 × 2 | 2 × 6 | 12 | 10 × 2 | 2 × 10 | 20 |
| 3 × 2 | 2 × 3 | 6 | 7 × 2 | 2 × 7 | 14 | | | |
| 4 × 2 | 2 × 4 | 8 | 8 × 2 | 2 × 8 | 16 | 0 × 2 | 2 × 0 | 0 |

## Practice

Cover the grid above. Fill in the missing numbers in the boxes.

4 × 2 = ☐        2 × 8 = ☐        2 × 5 = ☐

3 × 2 = ☐        2 × 5 = ☐        6 × 2 = ☐

6 × 2 = ☐        2 × 7 = ☐        2 × 9 = ☐

5 × 2 = ☐        2 × 2 = ☐        7 × 2 = ☐

9 × 2 = ☐        2 × 10 = ☐        2 × 6 = ☐

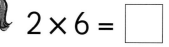

Now check your answers.

## Challenge

How many twos in 12?        What is half of 8?        How many twos in 8?

## Look and learn

Fractions are part of a whole.

$\frac{1}{2}$

not $\frac{1}{2}$

$\frac{1}{4}$

not $\frac{1}{4}$

## Practice

Colour $\frac{1}{2}$ of each shape.

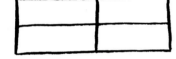

Colour $\frac{1}{2}$ of each shape.

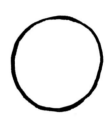
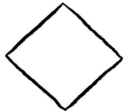

## Challenge

Colour $\frac{1}{4}$ of each shape. Make each pattern different.

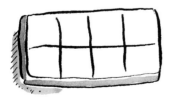

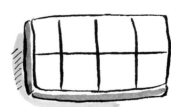

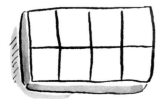

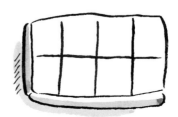

## Look and learn

Do you know how many centimetres there are in a metre?

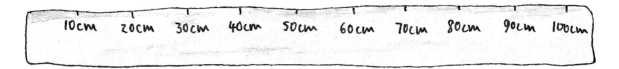

1 metre = 100 centimetres          1 m = 100 cm

## Practice

Join these to the most likely label.

about 1 metre

about 2 metres

about 10 cm

more than 2 metres

about 50 cm

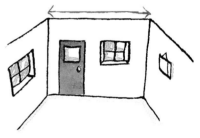

## Challenge

Guess how long each worm is.

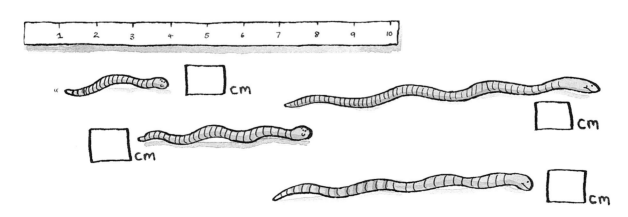

☐ cm

☐ cm

☐ cm

☐ cm

21

## Look and learn

Pictograms use pictures to show information.

| | | |
|---|---|---|
| apples: | 😊 😊 😊 😊 | 4 |
| pears: | 😊 😊 | 2 |
| oranges: | 😊 😊 😊 😊 😊 | 5 |

This was a survey of children who liked different fruit.

## Practice

This pictogram shows the favourite ice creams of a group of children.

| | |
|---|---|
| chocolate | 🍦 🍦 🍦 🍦 🍦 🍦 |
| mint | 🍦 🍦 🍦 |
| vanilla | 🍦 🍦 🍦 🍦 |
| strawberry | 🍦 🍦 🍦 🍦 🍦 |

How many children chose vanilla? ☐

How many children chose strawberry? ☐

Which is the most popular flavour? ☐

How many children were there altogether? ☐

Collect your own data to draw a pictogram showing favourite flavours of crisps.

## Look and learn

Use the number line to compare and order numbers.

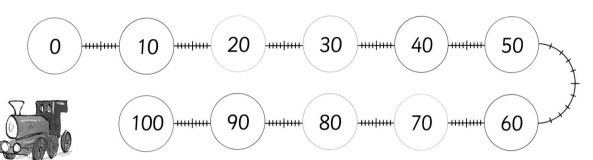

## Practice

Write the numbers that come between each pair of circles.

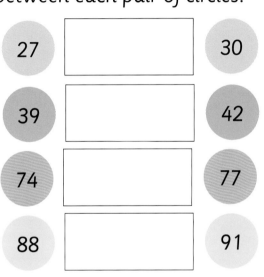

27 [ ] 30

39 [ ] 42

74 [ ] 77

88 [ ] 91

Circle the bigger number in each pair of numbers.

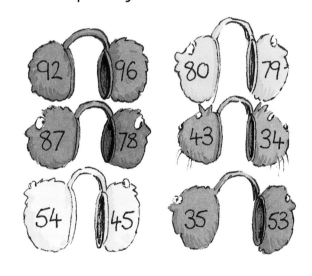

92  96

80  79

87  78

43  34

54  45

35  53

## Challenge

Write the numbers in the circles in order. Start with the smallest.

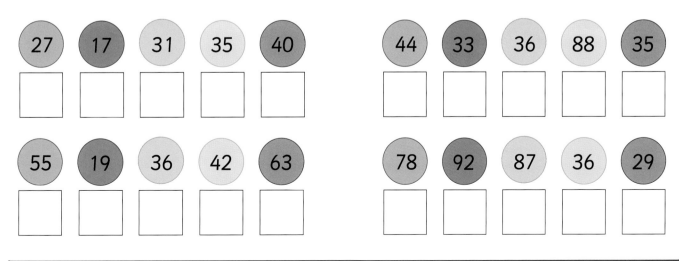

27  17  31  35  40          44  33  36  88  35

[ ] [ ] [ ] [ ] [ ]          [ ] [ ] [ ] [ ] [ ]

55  19  36  42  63          78  92  87  36  29

[ ] [ ] [ ] [ ] [ ]          [ ] [ ] [ ] [ ] [ ]

## Look and learn

Look at the addition and subtraction facts for this number trio.

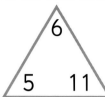

$$6 + 5 = 11$$
$$5 + 6 = 11$$

$$11 - 6 = 5$$
$$11 - 5 = 6$$

## Practice

Write the addition and subtraction facts for each of these.

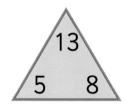

**Triangle: 13, 5, 8**

5 + ☐ = ☐

☐ + 5 = ☐

☐ − 5 = ☐

☐ − ☐ = 5

**Triangle: 15, 6, 9**

☐ + ☐ = 15

☐ + 6 = 15

15 − ☐ = ☐

15 − ☐ = ☐

**Triangle: 17, 9, 8**

9 + ☐ = ☐

☐ + 9 = ☐

☐ − ☐ = 9

☐ − 9 = ☐

## Challenge

Complete these addition grids.

| + | 9 | 8 | 7 |
|---|---|---|---|
| 6 | 15 |  |  |
| 2 |  |  |  |
| 8 |  |  |  |

| + | 3 | 7 | 9 |
|---|---|---|---|
| 8 |  |  |  |
| 4 |  | 11 |  |
|  |  |  | 8 |

| + | 9 | 11 | 15 |
|---|---|----|----|
| 6 |  |  |  |
| 2 |  | 13 |  |
| 8 | 17 |  |  |

## Look and learn

A number line can help you work out calculations.

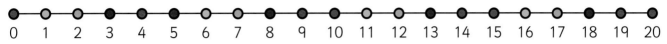

```
0  1  2  3  4  5  6  7  8  9  10  11  12  13  14  15  16  17  18  19  20
```

Remember, try 'hopping' your finger along the line when you work sums out.

## Practice

Here is an addition wall. Now work these out.

```
    15
  8    7
 3   5   2
```

```
  5   5   2
```

```
   4   6   2
```

```
      5
  8       3
```

```
  20
    12
       5
```

```
   20
  15
    5
```

```
      20
        14
   3
```

## Challenge

Find a place for the jelly numbers. Choose six different numbers.

0  1  2  3  4  5  6  7  8  9

 + 3 = 5     − 1 = ☐

5 + ☐ − 9    ☐ − 8 = ☐

## Look and learn

Look at these symmetrical shapes.

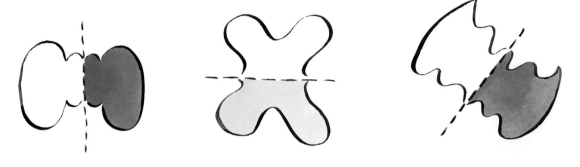

## Practice

Draw in a line of symmetry on each shape.

## Challenge

Complete the symmetry picture.

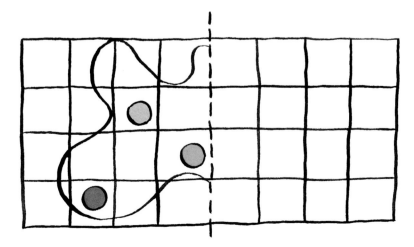

# Odd and even numbers

## Look and learn

You need to be able to recognise **odd** and **even** numbers.

| **even** | 2 | 4 | 6 | 8 | 10 | 12 | 14 | 16 → |
|---|---|---|---|---|---|---|---|---|
| **odd** | 1 | 3 | 5 | 7 | 9 | 11 | 13 | 15 → |

## Practice

Tick all the odd numbers.

Circle all the even numbers.

## Challenge

What digits do odd numbers end with?

Write a big odd number.

What digits do even numbers end with?

Write a big even number.

## Look and learn

It is useful to be able to add the values of coins.

Remember, try to recognise their shapes to make it easier.

## Practice

How much money is in each piggybank?

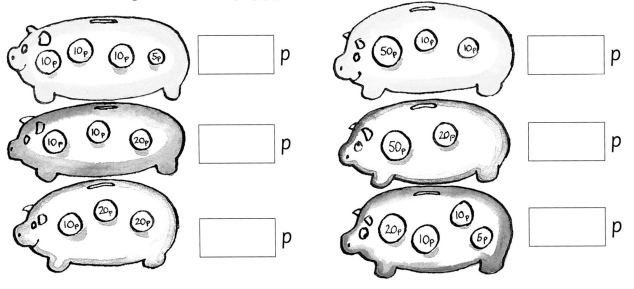

## Challenge

Write each of these totals.

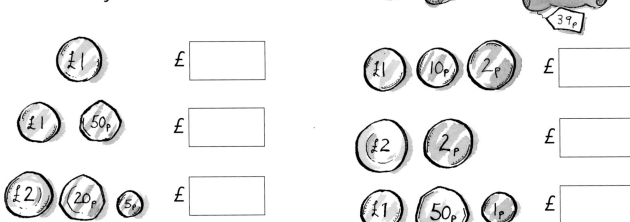

# 10 times table

## Look and learn

Learn the 10 times table.

| 1 × 10 | 10 × 1 | 10 | 5 × 10 | 10 × 5 | 50 | 9 × 10 | 10 × 9 | 90 |
|--------|--------|----|--------|--------|----|--------|--------|----|
| 2 × 10 | 10 × 2 | 20 | 6 × 10 | 10 × 6 | 60 | 10 × 10 | 10 × 10 | 100 |
| 3 × 10 | 10 × 3 | 30 | 7 × 10 | 10 × 7 | 70 | | | |
| 4 × 10 | 10 × 4 | 40 | 8 × 10 | 10 × 8 | 80 | 0 × 10 | 10 × 0 | 0 |

## Practice

Complete these 10 times table calculations.

1 × 10 = ☐          10 × 2 = ☐           5 × 10 = ☐

5 × 10 = ☐          10 × 4 = ☐          10 × 6 = ☐

3 × 10 = ☐          10 × 6 = ☐          8 × 10 = ☐

9 × 10 = ☐          10 × 8 = ☐          10 × 7 = ☐

7 × 10 = ☐          10 × 10 = ☐          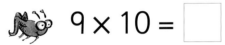 9 × 10 = ☐

## Challenge

Work these out.

How many tens in 30? ☐

How many threes in 30? ☐

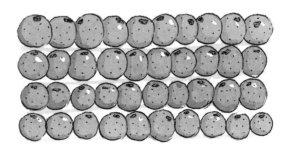

How many tens in 40? ☐

How many fours in 40? ☐

## Look and learn

$\frac{1}{2}$ of 8 = 4

$\frac{1}{4}$ of 8 = 2

## Practice

Circle $\frac{1}{2}$ of each set.
Write the answers.

$\frac{1}{2}$ of 6 = ☐

$\frac{1}{2}$ of 4 = ☐

$\frac{1}{2}$ of 10 = ☐

Complete the other half of the shield.

$\frac{1}{2}$ of ☐ = 2

$\frac{1}{2}$ of ☐ = 4

$\frac{1}{2}$ of ☐ = 3

## Challenge

Colour $\frac{1}{4}$ of each rectangle.

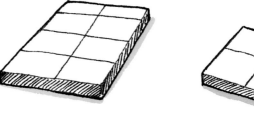

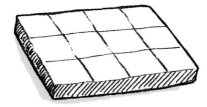
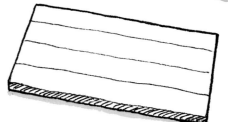

# Time

## Look and learn

These pairs of clocks show the same times.

**3:00**   **4:30**   **2:15**   **9:45**

## Practice

Write how many minutes are between each of these times.

  ☐      ☐

  ☐      ☐

  ☐      ☐

## Challenge

Complete these.

1 week = ☐ days          1 day = ☐ hours

1 year = ☐ months        1 hour = ☐ minutes

1 year = ☐ weeks         1 minute = ☐ seconds

# Data: tables

## Look and learn

Information is sometimes put into tables. Read the table to see who owns which pets.

| | dog | cat | hamster | fish |
|---|---|---|---|---|
| John | ✓ | | | |
| Mei Mei | | ✓ | | ✓ |
| Hamid | ✓ | ✓ | ✓ | |
| June | ✓ | ✓ | ✓ | ✓ |

## Practice

This is a table of children's names.

| 3 letters | 4 letters | 5 letters | 6 letters | 7 letters |
|---|---|---|---|---|
| Ben | Paul | Peter | Alison | Malcolm |
| Ali | John | Sarah | George | Kenneth |
| Lyn | Karl | Louis | Robert | Kerstin |
| Sue | Mick | Sally | Susane | Melinda |
| Pip | | Hamid | Warren | Deborah |
| | | | Sharon | Chelsea |
| | | | Pierre | |

Add your own name [              ]

1. How many names have 4 letters? [   ]

2. How many names have 6 letters? [   ]

3. How many letters does your name have? [   ]

4. How many names have more than 4 letters? [   ]

5. How many names have less than 5 letters? [   ]